THE
CUT THROAT
TRIAL

S. J. FLEET is the bestselling author also known as The Secret Barrister, a junior barrister specializing in criminal law. They write for many publications and are the author of the award-winning blog of the same name. Their first book, *The Secret Barrister: Stories of the Law and How It's Broken*, was a *Sunday Times* number one bestseller and spent more than a year in the top-ten bestseller charts. It won the Books Are My Bag Non-Fiction Award and was shortlisted for Waterstones Book of the Year and the Specsavers Non-Fiction Book of the Year. *Fake Law: The Truth About Justice in an Age of Lies* and *Nothing But the Truth: The Memoir of an Unlikely Lawyer* were instant *Sunday Times* top-ten bestsellers on publication. *The Cut Throat Trial* is their first novel.

Also by S. J. Fleet

Writing as The Secret Barrister:

The Secret Barrister: Stories of the Law and How It's Broken

Fake Law: The Truth About Justice in an Age of Lies

Nothing But the Truth: The Memoir of an Unlikely Lawyer

S. J. FLEET

THE CUT THROAT TRIAL

PICADOR

First published 2024 by Picador
an imprint of Pan Macmillan
The Smithson, 6 Briset Street, London EC1M 5NR
EU representative: Macmillan Publishers Ireland Ltd, 1st Floor,
The Liffey Trust Centre, 117–126 Sheriff Street Upper,
Dublin 1, D01 YC43
Associated companies throughout the world
www.panmacmillan.com

ISBN 978-1-0350-4668-3 HB
ISBN 978-1-0350-4669-0 TPB

1 3 5 7 9 8 6 4

A CIP catalogue record for this book is available from the British Library.

Printed and bound by CPI Group (UK) Ltd, Croydon, CR0 4YY

Visit www.picador.com to read more about all our books
and to buy them. You will also find features, author interviews and
news of any author events, and you can sign up for e-newsletters
so that you're always first to hear about our new releases.

THE
CUT THROAT
TRIAL

**Exhibit LJD/1/140225 – Extract from download
of iPhone JP/22/010125**

28 December 2024

- *IMAGE SENT*
- *Wat dat?*
- Bro, u wanna play a game?
- *Wat game G*
- Need 3 2 play
- *K*
- Basically we all bang sum1 out . . .
- *Ye?*
- but only 1 at a time
- *Wat u mean?*
- So like u hit him then I hit him and we go round circle til sum1 wins
- *How u win?*
- Lol when he's dead u daft fuk
- *Sick bro*
- Srsly, u up for that?
- *Haha yeman maybe*
- NYE?

[END OF MESSAGES]

1

Exhibit NR/2/310125 – Audio recording linked to Crime Report 81033112/24

[TRANSCRIPT]

31 December 2023, 23:59

OPERATOR: Police emergency.

CALLER: Hi. There's somebody . . . oh god. There's somebody on the street outside and [INAUDIBLE] knife.

OPERATOR: Can you repeat that, please.

CALLER: There's [INAUDIBLE] outside my flat and I think they've hit someone with a massive knife.

OPERATOR: Have you witnessed this?

CALLER: Course I fucking have, that's why I'm calling the police.

OPERATOR: Sir, if . . .

CALLER: Sorry, I don't mean to . . . I'm just, it's still going on, and I can't even see what . . .

OPERATOR: Sir, please just try to remain calm and answer my questions.

CALLER: Sorry.

OPERATOR: Where are you right now?

CALLER: I'm in my living room, it's a first floor flat. I can see out of my [INAUDIBLE] now round the corner, but I'm sure I saw him [INAUDIBLE] with the knife.

OPERATOR: What's your address?

CALLER: It's 112A Rowe Street. It's the flat above the laundrette.

OPERATOR: And who have you seen?

CALLER: There was a group of lads and an older bloke. I don't know what's happened but there was a lot of shouting and, when I looked out, one of them's got this massive knife, [INAUDIBLE] sword and he's waving it and trying to get [INAUDIBLE].

OPERATOR: Can you still see these lads?

CALLER: I can [INAUDIBLE] run off, but [INAUDIBLE] at least three. [INAUDIBLE] coming back from the alley.

OPERATOR: Can you see the man who you think was hit?

CALLER: No. I think he's still round the corner. [INAUDIBLE] going back.

OPERATOR: Can you . . .

CALLER: [INAUDIBLE] smashing, like glass breaking.

OPERATOR: You can hear glass breaking?

CALLER: Yeah. Sorry. You were asking something.

OPERATOR: Can you describe the person with the knife?

CALLER: Young, early twenties maybe. White.

OPERATOR: What was he wearing?

CALLER: Black, I think. I don't know. They all had hoods.

OPERATOR: What about the others? Can you describe them?

CALLER: I dunno, sorry. It was all so fast. I just know [INAUDIBLE] of them.

OPERATOR: The police are on their way. Is this number . . .

CALLER: [SHOUTING] Fucking hell!

OPERATOR: What's happening?

CALLER: [INAUDIBLE SHOUTING]

OPERATOR: OK, please just stay where you are. The police are on their way. Is this your mobile number that you're ringing from?

CALLER: No, it's [INAUDIBLE] girlfriend's. She's [INAUDIBLE].

OPERATOR: Are you OK to stay on the line, please, until the police arrive?

CALLER: [INAUDIBLE]

[CALL DISCONNECTED]

Ableford Crown Court is a shithole.

That assertion, whether or not rooted in truth, can at least be said to endure, scribed as it has been in four-foot-high faded fuchsia on the building's concrete fascia for ten years and two months. Whether it followed or inspired the Tripadvisor review posted in identical terms around the same time is a subject of occasional speculation among regulars, but the efforts at deletion by the court administration have been equally ineffective.

If evidence were being sought for the proposition, however, the court's exterior might be a fertile starting point. In a spasm of 1960s permissiveness, Ableford Metropolitan Borough Council granted consent for the town's four-roomed red-brick magistrates' courthouse to be extended into a state-of-the-art 'combined court centre', a sprawling complex intended to accommodate twelve new Crown Courtrooms. The battle between brutalism and Victorian was ultimately resolved in favour of the former, and giant panels of raw concrete were erected in what the developer described as 'bold geometric forms', but which a passing tourist might mistake for an approximation of a child experimenting for the first time with Duplo. The completed extension most closely resembled a half-finished multi-storey car park with added, inexplicable glass; in this case, wall-to-ceiling windows running the perimeter of the first floor, exposing the administrative offices boxed within to the glare of the onlooking public, should any of those members of the public harbour any curiosity as to what court administrators do at their cubicles.

What the outside walls lack in charm, they more than atone for in rust-streaked water staining, which has the unintended advantage of disguising much of the older, more conservatively coloured graffiti. Whatever epithets they might contain are at least not immediately visible to the naked eye.

The building's extension was expected to generate a heavy daily footfall, and ease of entry and egress at peak times might have been aided by – to quote one regular patron of the criminal courts – the installation of more than 'one single fucking revolving door'. Even more so if that door was not prone to sticking with such regularity that the glass has already had to be replaced three times this year, fractured on each occasion by an angrily thrust palm. Patience is not always abundant with those patrons. But that is barristers for you.

Airport-style security has been a relatively recent addition to the process of entry. As a result, attendees can expect to queue around the building for twenty minutes to pass through an archway detector and be interrogated, frisked and relieved of their contraband by a security team led by self-appointed 'head bouncer' Annette, a five-foot engine room whose time served in this building corralling society's least desirable has given rise to her own lore and law.

Locals still revel in the fate of one visitor several years back, who, anticipating an unhappy outcome before a famously difficult judge, arrived at the back of the lunchtime queue brimming with a morning's worth of Dutch courage and a tenner's worth of Colombia's own. Seeing the size of the queue before him, he staggered round to the fire-exit door and manoeuvred himself through, announcing to the onrushing security that they could go fuck themselves, actually, because he was, in fact, a fucking King Daddy who could not be late for his sentence in front of 'that fat bell-end in Court 5'. Annette dropped him to the floor and – depending on who is narrating the story – either knocked the man out cold (Annette) or sat awkwardly on his legs for eight seconds until the court police officer arrived (every other witness). Whichever version is preferred, the man does not emerge well. But that is barristers for you.

Inside the court building, the grand, green-carpeted marble staircase that greets you as you pass through security is best not climbed; it leads to a first-floor door marked 'RESTRICTED ACCESS', and then up to a second-floor door marked 'RESTRICTED ACCESS'. Only when you reach the third floor is it a different story: there is no marking on the door, but a firm push will confirm that access to what lies behind is, indeed, restricted.

No, to go anywhere that court users might wish or need go, one must travel down an undesignated corridor to the left, through four sets of double doors and past the darkened, long-disused canteen, from within which a redundant hum can still be heard. A hum of a different kind also pervades the corridors: an ever-present whiff of hospital ammonia, notable not only for the thwack it reliably delivers to the back of the throat, but for the absence of evidence of any cleaning that might explain it. A bushel of mushrooms sprouting against the skirting board stands as a defiant testament to when this part of the building last encountered a mop.

Through the final pair of doors, a less splendid flight of concrete steps heaves into view, adjoining an unburdened lift. This – 'the Grand Staircase', as it has been named – spirals up to four floors of corridors, each corridor boasting three courtrooms, each courtroom's interior an identikit hybrid of faux-Victorian features and lacquered pine, as if a nineteenth-century architect had run out of inspiration halfway through and made a frantic trolley dash through Ikea.

Whether by design or accident, no natural light is permitted entry to the courtrooms. This prohibition extends to the entrance doors being fashioned out of heavy slabs of timber with no window slots, so a passer-by wishing to discreetly see what is happening within has to haul open the doors and reveal themselves, the whine of the hinges liable to rudely interrupt whatever is proceeding.

Were such a passer-by in residence today, and had they scaled to the heights of the fourth floor, and had they walked along the chipped tiled corridor towards Courtroom 11, and had they taken the risk of heaving open the door, what they could expect to rudely interrupt right now, as the morning's business draws towards its end, is the reading of an indictment. This exercise might not, immediately, strike the passer-by as significant or interesting. But it bears a moment's attention.

The reading of an indictment by a court clerk to a defendant – or, on this particular day and in this particular case, more than one defendant – may sound like a fusty formality, but it heralds something important: a jury is being put in charge of a defendant's destiny. A defendant – or, on this particular day and in this particular case, three defendants – is each having their liberty placed in the hands of twelve strangers, who right now know nothing about the accused, and nothing about what they are said to have done, other than the snapshot that is teased by the formal reading of the charges that the indictment discloses.

It is the start of a process in which the lives of those twelve strangers, and the persons they are judging, will become inextricably bound and for ever entangled. It is a voyage on which the jurors and defendants travel together, but which will end with those at the wheel deciding the fate of those riding pillion. They will not speak, these two groups; indeed, a threat of imprisonment hangs over any juror who solicits any conversation with, or poses any question to, the persons now in their charge. Instead, the information that the strangers are deemed to require, and the rules that they must follow, will be filtered, moderated and debated by bewigged lawyers with no personal interest in the outcome.

But in charge those twelve strangers are. They are, as of right now, in charge not merely figuratively but literally. They each carry personal responsibility for taking decisions that will never be reasoned or justified to those affected, but that will irreversibly fix the course of three human lives. More than three, of course, because the stakes in the verdicts that these twelve will be required to reach are incalculably high, not only for the blank faces in the dock and those whom they are said to have wronged, but for all of us who tell ourselves that we walk our streets safe under the protection of the criminal law.

This is the start of a murder trial.

A trial in which fingers will be pointed not only by the state, but by the three defendants, each looking to secure his freedom by foisting blame onto his co-accused.

A cut throat trial.

Let the game begin.

S. J. FLEET

URN 08AF0468325

INDICTMENT

IN THE CROWN COURT AT ABLEFORD

THE KING – v – CRAIG MERVYN-SCOTT, ARRON FREEMAN AND JAMAL LOWTON

CRAIG MERVYN-SCOTT, ARRON FREEMAN and JAMAL LOWTON are charged as follows:

Count 1
STATEMENT OF OFFENCE

MURDER.

PARTICULARS OF OFFENCE

CRAIG MERVYN-SCOTT, ARRON FREEMAN and JAMAL LOWTON on the 1st day of January 2025 murdered Bernard Hooper.

Count 2
STATEMENT OF OFFENCE

HAVING AN OFFENSIVE WEAPON, contrary to section 1(1) of the Prevention of Crime Act 1953.

10

PARTICULARS OF OFFENCE

CRAIG MERVYN-SCOTT, ARRON FREEMAN and JAMAL LOWTON cn the 1st day of January 2025 had with them in a public place, namely Rowe Street, Ableford, an offensive weapon, namely a 'zombie' knife.

Officer of the Court

PART I

———

THE PROSECUTION CASE

CHAPTER 1

Aliyah (The Prosecutor)

The air feels tight as I survey the benches to my right. The sensation never dulls, not for me at least. Ever since my first opening speech in my first magistrates' court trial – prosecuting a woman caught leaving Asda with forty pounds of sirloin steak in her knickers – I've never lost that buzz, that sting of nervous energy surging from my stomach and dispersing out to every toe and every fingertip.

The prosecution opening is the prosecutor's opportunity to set the scene. You get to define the parameters of what is to follow, to implant in your audience the narrative that will then play out before them as the evidence unfolds. It is the prosecution's advantage, as I like to remind juries when I am defending. The prosecution tells the jury what will happen, and then produces evidence which fits with what the jury has been told will happen, and a convincing but wholly illusory confirmation is subtly engineered. The jurors feel immediate sympathy towards the prosecution witnesses because what they are saying fits the story the jury has been told.

You need to build trust, right from the outset. From before your first word. From the moment the panel of prospective jurors file into court, staring around them at the bewigged and begowned figures on counsel's row and taking in the underwhelming faux-majesty of our eighties-chic courtroom, it is imperative to maintain composure. Supress that energy, maintain poker rigidity. It's why I wear flats in court. It's not as if I need the height, and they allow me to plant my soles flush to the floor, both hands on the bench in front of me, palms pushing down. It earths me, channelling the adrenaline down to the ground as I sit and wait for my moment. When I eventually rise to speak, I will find a side panel or a chair leg with the outside of my foot – whichever is available – and push outwards, as hard as I can. An old trick taught by my pupilmaster twenty-five years ago. *It stops you from jiggling*, he had whispered to me, his fingers curling around my thigh as he demonstrated his technique.

Forty pounds in value, I should clarify. Sterling, not weight. Four steaks each costing a tenner, you might just have a hope of smuggling past a distracted supermarket security guard. Eighteen kilogrammes of vacuum-packed meat – few heroin addicts are quite that ambitious. No, it was four packs of supermarket luxury-brand sirloins, inevitably to sell down the pub. Always *down* the pub. Never *up* the pub. Purloined sirloin. For the bargainous combined cost of a single wrap. A precious ten-pound note, to be immediately, desperately converted into the instantaneous warmth that a shot of muddy street purity diamorphine intravenously delivers. Detached relief for a few hours, until the effects wear off and the cycle begins anew. Back to Asda for the next round of *Steak to Smack*.

It is important to be accurate. It is important to be precise. It is the smallest detail on which a criminal trial can hinge. A loose word from a witness, an ambiguity in a formal admission, an ill-chosen expression from an advocate – the slightest vagary in the weather can turn the climate for good. This is why my opening speech is always written verbatim. Every word is road-tested. Any ambiguity neutralised. The craft is hidden, but it is essential. I want the jury to accept unquestioningly what I am telling them. They may come to doubt parts of it as the evidence unravels and witnesses buckle under cross-examination, but the stronger the narrative I can construct now, the greater chance of the foundations holding when the defence bulldozers move in.

I lift my head slightly and observe the jury. One or two are displaying the first signs of restlessness, a bit too eager to get into the action. Most are staring obediently at the judge. Well, not long now, ladies and gentlemen. His Honour Judge Letts is approaching the end of his introductory homily, and the minutes until my opening are receding into seconds.

Tick. Tick. Tick.

There is a side that Jeremy Letts saves especially for us, the professionals. But with a jury, he is sweetness and temperance incarnate. The very image of a people's judge. Fair, open-minded and accommodating, but also willing to give the bad guys a damn hard kicking if the press gallery is occupied. *We try this case together*, he tells the assembled fourteen. *You are the judges of the facts, I am the judge of the law.* The obligatory warnings against jurors conducting personal research on the internet or social media are denuded by practised chuckles and affected affability, right down to the knowing reference to 'social media sites such as Myspace – or, as I am given to understand is now more popular – The TikTok', a minor defiance of expectations guaranteed to raise a smile among the younger jurors.

I am your captain for this flight, is the tenor of his pitch to the jury. Well, fuck off, Jeremy. This is my plane. And I have been studiously watching the passengers, planning how best to get them on board.

Identifying the foreman-in-waiting is key. Since the panel entered the courtroom, I have been making calculated assumptions based on their age, sex, race and, in particular, the way in which they swore their oath or affirmation when reading the card handed to them by the usher. Anybody stumbling over the words or having to be asked by the judge to repeat themselves after omitting or mangling the construction – they are out of the picture as far as who gets to play foreman. *I will faithfully try the defendant* is a reliable litmus; insert a superfluous 'to' after 'try' and they will always stumble, a failure of their not having understood the meaning of the solemn vow they are making. I will still try to engage those stragglers, of course. I cannot afford to lose any of the twelve votes. I will look into their eyes and smile gently when I am addressing them, ensuring to keep my language precise yet accessible, but they will not be the centre of my world. That will instead be the foreman; the man or woman who has not yet been elected by their peers, but whose confidence, demeanour, dress and accent persuades me of that inescapable destiny. My initial impression may change as the trial progresses, and the jurors' attentiveness or distraction is betrayed by the furious taking of notes or the drooping of eyelids, but my instinct is usually correct.

I am in the zone. Laser focus. That is what is required. That is what a case of this gravity demands. Nothing less.

Prosecuting, you see, is about fairness. It is about measure. It is a calling. And I take it seriously. Empathy is my prosecutorial style. Remembering, at every turn, the enormous privilege that I have.

Prosecuting, by definition, is a privilege that confers immense power. You are conducting the might of the state, flexing the coercive muscle of thousands of police officers and thousands of prosecuting lawyers, all gathering under the banner of the Crown.

As prosecuting counsel, I am the Crown's representative. And I must always act in a way consistent with the weight of that responsibility.

But, more than that, I must be mindful of my own advantages, and the disadvantages that almost always accumulate in the lives of those I am prosecuting. I must not use my education to belittle or humiliate. I must not make assumptions, nor encourage assumptions among juries, based on a defendant's background or appearance. I must make allowances for the hardships that defendants may have encountered, and, importantly, must be seen by the jury to be doing so as well.

This is how I gain the jury's trust. I am not Robo Prosecutor, pitilessly gunning down any strays in my path. I understand these people's lives. My cross-examination is intended to be quietly devastating; no shouting or badgering, much less crowing or insulting. I prosecute in sorrow, not in anger.

Take these three boys in the dock, right now. Boys. Seventeen, each of them. They are accused of something truly wicked, but they are, at the same time, still children, in the eyes of the law at least. There can be no doubt that they are scared. There is no doubt of the disparity between our lots in life. Their advantages are few, mine are many. I have read the Social Services material, the psychological reports, the intermediary assessments. I can recite the litany of educational and social misfortunes that have defined their existences. I know, from my own experience of defending children just like these, the absence of opportunity to escape their circumstances. I know that if they have been broken, they have been broken on the axis of the society into which they were born.

And so, I will treat them fairly. With consideration and respect and compassion. Even when I am doubting them with my questions, and disbelieving them in my speeches, I will do so with civility and moderation and even-handedness. The defence barristers enjoy greater latitude; they may ramp up the pathos and let passion run free. But not me. My bywords are calmness and empathy. My voice will ooze patience, my deportment will radiate calm. For this is what the Crown, and the jury, expect.

I will be the grown-up in the room. I will be the jury's Sherpa, and they my confidantes. I will hold their hands throughout the trial, modulating my every word and reminding them with modesty and humbleness that *it's entirely a matter for you whether you agree with my arguments. Entirely a matter for you.*

And, at every stage, I will be doing everything in my power to convict these feral little fuckers of murder.

CHAPTER 2

The Prosecution Opening

The jurors appear to sense the imminent descent. One, a tall woman in her early forties, rotates her neck, shaking loose the stiffness built up over the preceding eighteen minutes. Juror number twelve, separated from his brethren by an empty seat strapped in yellow and black tape, clasps his hands together and stretches them in front of him, the bulge in his throat betraying a strangled yawn. A contagious shuffling of papers suddenly breaks out across the front row.

The judge is still talking, but something in his pace and tone indicates that it is a matter of moments before the action begins, and the prosecution opening speech spills the full details of a case that many of the jurors have already seen trailed in the national press. A juicy muse for editorial thunders of Broken Britain; of a lawless underclass visiting its violent anarchy upon the unsuspecting sensibilities of Middle England, or of an uncaring society confronted by the grimly inevitable product of entrenched deprivation and inequality.

They have listened attentively to the instructions from the bench. One pair of eyes on the back row appears trained downwards, the twitch of an elbow suggestive of a touchscreen being swiped. But for the most part, the jurors appear engaged, alert and itching to crack on.

Finally – the words drop, and all twenty-eight ears in the jury box prick up in unison – the judge extends special thanks to the two extra jurors, who have been invited to stay for the opening speech in case one of the selected twelve discovers overnight that they are not in fact available to stay for the extended four-week duration. He volunteers an amusing anecdote about a juror in a 'multi-handed section 18 wounding' who returned on the second day to report that her agreement to sit for a six-week trial had caused conniptions when she arrived home and told her boyfriend, who was forced to reveal the surprise engagement trip to New York that he had spent six months arranging. The judge's slip into legalese does not distract from the point that he probably was not intending to make: You don't have to even set foot in a court for the criminal justice system to fuck up your life.

Fucked-up lives are, of course, the life blood of the criminal courts. Nobody would be in this room without them. And while that is not the expression that Aliyah Arshad deploys as she rises and turns to the jury with a slightly awkward half-smile, it will never be far from the surface as she outlines the prosecution case, nor, indeed, during the weeks of evidence that lie ahead. It is a truth that all fourteen jurors will struggle to evade, try as they might to maintain the clinical dividing line between what happens in court and their own, real lives. Few people want to be confronted with the facts; the visceral horrors of the world. Nobody wants to acknowledge that life – their life – is so acutely, terrifyingly vulnerable.

For now, however, such tensions have yet to trouble this jury. They are still in cinema mode, excited for the drama that is about to unfold. They are not yet dealing with real lives; their fingertips are not yet tracing real blood.

Straightening her black silk robe as she towers over her lectern,

Aliyah Arshad dispenses the formal introductions. She prosecutes, on behalf of the Crown. Her learned friend Mr Wyatt of King's Counsel represents the first defendant, Craig Mervyn-Scott. Mr Evans of King's Counsel represents the interests of the second defendant, Arron Freeman, and Miss Rennie represents the interests of the third defendant, Jamal Lowton. His Honour, the Learned Judge, presides over the trial to ensure that it is conducted fairly. And the three defendants, by convention, sit in the dock.

Each juror surrenders to the instinct to turn their heads towards the characters as they are introduced; from the barristers, bewigged and sitting in benched rows running the width of the courtroom, the prosecutor furthest from the jury box, the defence barristers closest; to the judge's bench, front and centre and raised high above the well of the court; to the floor-to-ceiling Perspex screen at the back of the room, and the three small figures sitting mutely behind, heads bowed and flanked by thick-set security staff.

What Aliyah is about to say, she tells the jurors, is not evidence in the case, but a summary of what the prosecution say the evidence will prove.

And then, turning, almost imperceptibly, so that her eyes meet juror number seven – white male, late forties, tortoiseshell glasses, open-necked long-sleeved blue shirt and smart dark-grey slacks – Aliyah begins the tale of New Year's Eve 2024.

It was a bitterly cold evening, one which the jurors may well remember. The city had been carpeted in a thick blanket of snow, causing havoc for many people's celebrations.

Rita Hooper certainly remembers it. It was the night that she and her husband, Bernard, a retired teacher, had to revise their plans to go and see friends because they couldn't get their old Vauxhall Astra out in the snow. It was the night that she gave Bernard a quick kiss

23

goodbye as he popped out to the supermarket to grab a bottle of champagne for them to share as they saw in the New Year. That was to be the last time Rita would give her husband a quick kiss good-bye. It was the last time she would see him alive. They would never get to see in the New Year.

Aliyah Arshad pauses, allowing the staccato sentences to fall through the air like snowflakes, and waiting for them to settle, break and dissolve. Every back in the jury box is upright, and every face pursed. No phones are being idly swiped now.

On his way back from the shop, Bernard Hooper had the terrible misfortune to encounter these three defendants. Aliyah raises her left arm, palm open, not moving herself but inviting the jury to turn their collective gaze towards the dock, the reinforced Perspex box in which three teenaged boys sit constrained by convention. Most of the jurors oblige. Number seven is still returning Aliyah's stare.

These three defendants had one thing, and one thing only, on their minds that night: to experience the thrill of violence in its most gratuitous, extreme and lethal form. High on cocaine, they armed themselves with weapons and headed into town. And when they happened across seventy-four-year-old Mr Hooper, they saw the opportunity to act out their twisted, vicious fantasies.

They pursued the lone Bernard Hooper down Rowe Street, steering him away from the safety of the revellers gathering as the clock ticked towards midnight. They led him away from the Christmas lights strung throughout the town centre, and lured him towards the darkness of a secluded alleyway, known as Garth Yard.

And then they armed themselves with *this*.

An eagle-eyed observer – or perhaps one with any bird's-eye view – might have already spotted a package on the seat to Aliyah Arshad's left. Bending slightly, she retrieves the prop – a large plastic cylinder – and holds it aloft with both hands, bending her elbows to lend emphasis to its weight. The dark item visible within still bears the discoloration of fingerprint powder, but the ornate shape and size are what deliver the impact.

'This,' Aliyah speaks more slowly, 'is an illegal weapon known as a "zombie knife" – because it is specifically designed and intended to cause fatal injuries.' She turns the protective cylinder over, affording the jury a first look at the sixteen-inch cutting edge curving upwards to a sharp point, and then at the twenty serrations on the other side. The word 'SLAUGHTER' emblazoned across the five-inch hilt cannot be seen through the protective packaging, but will be visible, the jurors are assured, in the photographs they will see.

This was the weapon used by the three defendants as they inflicted over sixty wounds to Bernard Hooper's head, face, torso and legs; a frenzied attack that lasted approximately five minutes. The post-mortem would later establish that he died of blood loss from those wounds, which severed major arteries in his neck. A pathologist had said that the nature of one such wound was consistent with an attempt – albeit unsuccessful – to sever Mr Hooper's head from his body. In other words, to decapitate him.

An audible murmur from juror number thirteen provokes a raised eyebrow from the bench, but no admonition, and appears to reflect the reaction of all fourteen. Many are now looking actively queasy. They receive Aliyah's recitation of the other blunt-force injuries – consistent with the use of other weapons, or with heavy and sustained punches and kicks – with blank, slightly green faces.

There will be evidence in abundance, Aliyah promises, from CCTV cameras and horrified eyewitnesses; and compelling forensic scientific evidence proving that each of the three defendants played their part in the murder.

But it is not only the evidence of third parties that the members of the jury will receive. 'A particularly callous feature of this case,' – she lowers her voice an octave – 'is that while Bernard Hooper lay dying on the ground, the defendants prodded his body with the knife, as his life slipped away, taunting him with the words: "How does it feel to die?"'

'We know this because we live – do we not, members of the jury? – in a social media age. And, after the defendants had done what they came to do, after they had exhausted themselves with the violence, they made a video recording of Mr Hooper's final moments; a digital trophy, to be shared across their social media channels. A preview of what the police would find when they arrived at Rowe Street: the three defendants coated in Bernard Hooper's blood, and the sixteen-inch blade embedded in his chest.

'This, the prosecution say, was killing for the sake of killing. A brutal and sadistic murder, committed by three young men who wanted to experience the thrill of taking a life, and of doing so in the most violent, bloody and merciless way they could imagine. They lured Bernard Hooper to his death, and they took their time – five whole minutes – in inflicting the numerous agonising, fatal injuries.'

As Aliyah Arshad takes a moment to turn the pages of the blue notebook on her lectern, one or two jurors gently exhale, perceiving a cue that the worst – for now at least – is over. It is a false hope. The prosecutor has barely begun. This is merely the start of her opening. The summary of the summary. The deeply unamusing amuse bouche.

But before the prosecutor is able to accelerate into the detail of the evidence that she will call, a motion from the dock catches the eye of the judge. A woman – early thirties, neat navy suit – is seated alongside the third defendant, Jamal Lowton, and is signalling with her hand, in what might best be described as a half-cocked royal wave. She is the intermediary assisting Jamal Lowton to understand and follow the proceedings, and is indicating that a break is required to aid Jamal's concentration.

The judge allows Arshad to reach a natural pause before gently interjecting, and inviting the jury to rise. As the jurors begin the 'exit shuffle' – a dance they perform as they move awkwardly along the narrow benches and in which they will become only too well rehearsed in the weeks that follow – gathering cardigans and stretching arms, the prosecutor's last words hang in the air, resistant to absorption.

'All three defendants deny that this was a joint attack. Each denies being a party to murder. And each has their own, very different account of how the defenceless, blameless Bernard Hooper met his fate.'

CHAPTER 3

Craig (The First Defendant)

The judge says we're having a break. Every forty minutes or something, my brief said. It's what the intermediary says Jamal needs, cos he's supposedly too fucked in the head to pay attention. It's a joke. He's not mental, it's the skunk. That's what's fucked his brain. Dickhead.

It's hard to listen to, don't get me wrong. I'm glad for a break. That prosecutor woman hasn't even begun, Arron whispers to me. There's hours left. Apparently this is just the introduction, like. Where she says in general 'this is what went down', so the jury think bad of us right from the beginning. But she's now going to tell the jury about all of the evidence, in detail. So like 'this witness says this, and that witness says that'. And that's before the witnesses even come in and say it themselves. So the jury are hearing this shit like three or four times. How is that fair? Three or four times for the jury to be told 'they're all guilty, they all killed the old man', when it didn't even go down like that. I get to say that once. If I'm allowed. My brief says we have to wait to decide if I even give evidence or not. Because, apparently, it's not always a good idea. I don't understand that. If I don't say something, surely the jury's gonna think it's because I'm guilty? But my brief says it's more complicated than that.

Probably they're worried that the prosecutor is going to make me look even more guilty. That's what she's paid for. Fucking million pounds a year or something to make people look guilty, even if they're not guilty. Asking trick questions and tripping them up. Making them say things they don't mean. Fuck that. My brief says the prosecutor's a complete bitch once she gets going. She doesn't look that scary though. All skinny and lanky with a big nose and a wobbly neck like a turkey, like fucking Big Bird. I was watching her fidgeting while the judge was talking. Reckon she's a smoker. She's got that twitch.

My mum was the same. Not my birth mum, obviously. But Paula. She was a forty-a-day woman, and the minute she started aching she was scratching and flicking her fingers like that, almost clicking them, without even noticing she was doing it. *Click click click.* Like her hand was trying to distract her brain from wanting a smoke. Once she'd started she couldn't stop, even when she'd got her smokes. She'd still be clicking in between drags. It used to drive my stepdads mental. All of them said it at one time or another. I didn't mind it myself. It was just her way. The sound was like a hoover or the fridge. Just a noise in the background letting you know it was there. I liked that. But not my stepdads. It put them on edge, like it meant they couldn't relax and watch the telly or have a blaze because she was just sitting there on the kitchen stool, *click click click.* Course, it was MJ who put an end to it. He put an end to a lot of things.

Maybe Big Bird is nervous. Maybe she's never prosecuted a murder before. My brief says she's only been a KC for like a year. If she's not done a murder before, maybe I've got a chance if I give evidence. Maybe she won't be as good at tripping me up. Making me look like I'm lying. I want the jury to hear things from my mouth, not just hers. Not just those witnesses who are lying through their teeth. And I don't want them to just hear from Arron or Jamal, because they're both doing me dirty. If I'm looking at life, I want that jury to look me in the eye while I tell them what I need to tell them.

It's like what I tried to tell my brief when I was in the police station. Cos I told him what had happened. Most of it, at least. The bits he needed to know. And I said I want to tell this to the police. But he said nah, go no comment. He said don't start telling the police things, because they can then use those things to make other things look bad.

So he wrote like a thing which I signed saying basically I haven't done nothing wrong, and he read it to the police when the interview started, and then when they kept asking me questions I just had to say no comment, over and over and over for like five hours or something. I don't even know what questions they were. I just said *no comment, no comment, no comment,* until the words meant nothing and it was just a sound I was making. I was falling asleep by the end of it. I'd been awake for two days straight.

We was all taken to different cop shops, far as I could tell. Arron and Jamal definitely didn't come with me, anyway. I was by myself in that van, listening to the siren blaring in my ears. The fed in the back with me made my handcuffs a bit looser when I said they were hurting. He seemed pretty sound. But then when I got to the police station, there was some other fed at the desk and he was a dick. I had to take off all my clothes, even my boxers, and they give me these police prison clothes that were absolutely rank. Stank of pure shit. And then they got this woman doctor who took my blood and my piss and stuck things under my nails and pulled out my hair. And then I had to show her all of my injuries, and there were a lot, obviously. Because of what happened.

Now the jury has gone and one of the barristers is standing up. The fat one, Arron's brief. He's pissed off about something that the prosecutor said in her speech. But he can't just say that. He can't speak in plain English. No, it's all lawyer. *'I wouldn't ordinarily seek to correct a comment made in opening, but I'm slightly concerned about the Crown's use of the word "blameless" to describe Mr Hooper, in light of the nature of my client's defence and the application that Your Honour has yet to determine.'*

All fucking code. Now my brief is getting up. He's not pissed, but the judge is asking, *'What do you say, Mr Wyatt?'* and I think he's saying he agrees. *'Certainly it is not my lay client's case that Mr Hooper's conduct was blameless, although, as Your Honour knows, for very different reasons.'* Big Bird looks fucked off. She's up on her feet.

'Your Honour, it's the Crown's opening. It is how the Crown puts its case. I am a little baffled by my learned friends' objections. The jury will hear how the defence cases are put and can in due course decide for themselves whether my chosen adjective is apt.'

How the fuck I'm supposed to follow this, I don't know. But at least it's better than listening to how that poor fucker died. Cos nobody deserves that. Not even him.

CHAPTER 4

Jennifer (Counsel for the Third Defendant)

I catch the courtroom door as it swings back towards me, my outstretched palm flashing in front of my face and taking the weight of the wood with a thud. Baxter Wyatt doesn't look back as he strides down the corridor ahead of me, his tall frame casting a spindly shadow over the faded terracotta tiles in his wake.

'Twat,' mutters a voice to my left, in what wouldn't even qualify as a stage whisper. I heave the door once, twice, three times until there is sufficient momentum for it to swing ajar long enough for my solicitor, Caz, to bob under my outstretched arm and out onto the concourse. I nip through after her and hold the door still for the crowd behind us as the courtroom empties.

'What would it have cost *him* to hold it?' Caz growls. 'Knowing that we're all right behind him? Is there something in the silks' handbook that says once you're in your tights you can't act like a member of civilised fucking society?'

'Serenity now,' I smile winningly at her.

The thunder on her face immediately melts and she grins conspiratorially. 'Insanity later,' she completes.

There are many, many things I love about my diminutive instructing solicitor. Her zero-fucks-given candour is obviously up there. The steady stream of grisly criminal cases that pay my mortgage, naturally. But her encyclopaedic ability to spot, decode and return an obscure 1990s sitcom reference is by some distance top of that list. It is, as I have told her many times, a remarkable, if utterly useless, sort of talent.

Bob Evans emerges at the threshold and hesitates, before stepping back to allow two women – press? Public gallery? I've not noticed them in court – to pass through before him. He then retreads his steps and thanks me humbly for my services to door-holding, nodding at Caz with a smile.

'I might pop across the road for a coffee-cheeno,' he says. 'Can I bring either of you anything?'

Caz doesn't even need to look at me before firmly declining on behalf of us both. Our plans for the next twenty minutes are set in stone.

'Wonderful!' Bob beams with unrestrained delight, as if instead of a fairly brusque refusal he'd just received an offer of a handjob in the canteen. 'I'll see if I can tempt Baxter into sin instead.'

'See?' I nod at Caz as Bob rolls away, the tails on his jacket flapping in his self-generated breeze. 'Some silks – very nice indeed.'

'Too nice.' She wrinkles her nose into an affected scowl. 'Can't see him really laying into a witness, can you? No grit. No . . .' She inelegantly shoves her laptop under her arm so that both hands are liberated for an entirely unnecessary and exaggerated mime as she loses her modulation and near enough shouts the word 'balls'.

Concerned for the fate of her MacBook, I gently tug the computer free and place it atop my own, and pointedly start walking down the hall. Hint taken, Caz follows.

Usually where there is a break in play, we would take the opportunity to speak to the client, but with Jamal buried under layers of Category A security in the cells, that is a futile endeavour in anything less than half an hour. Jamal has instead been told that Caz and I will come to see him at the start and end of each court day, and these precious twenty-minute segments are to be dedicated to a much more important pursuit.

'You got them on you?' Caz demands.

'I'm stopping by the robing room,' I reply, and she nods, satisfied. I can always be depended upon to keep my side of the bargain; a pact now fifteen years old, terms non-negotiable and set by Caz on the day we first met, as we stood outside Colchester Crown Court in the pissing rain, waiting for a gap in the torrent. While I rooted fruitlessly for an umbrella, Caz spied in my gaping bag the tell-tale ribbon on my depleted pack of Marlboro Gold, and that was that. Her hand was straight in.

'I'll keep you in briefs,' she stated, matter-of-factly, 'and you'll keep me in fags.' I nodded, instinctively withdrawing my Zippo and obediently holding it up, still trying to calibrate myself onto the same social plane as this five-foot, purple-haired pickpocket whose East End rasp put me in mind irrevocably of Alan Sugar. 'I don't like your chambers,' she exhaled hoarsely through silver plumes, pointing at my branded tote bag. 'But you're a Marlboro girl, so we can be friends.'

Since that chance encounter, Caz's boys have made up approximately half of my defence practice. Her knowledge of the families on the local estates, their histories and their labyrinthine family trees, their loyalties and their rivalries, their squabbles and the indecorous means and particular weapons by which those are resolved, is omniscient. The families adore Caz for her blunt speaking and respect her for her hard work, and her boutique firm – *'Don't ever say "small", it's fucking boutique, like me'* – turns over a heavy churn of very serious crime. Caz herself handles the bulk of the Youth Court work that Caroline Carter & Co. bring in, her control-freakery one of many attributes that bond us. Pride in her client care, although important, only tells part of the tale. There is an equally pressing commercial imperative, about which Caz is entirely open. *Dangerous boys turn into dangerous men.*

The Lowton family has had its share of dangerous boys dutifully so maturing. Prior to his arrest for murder, however, Jamal was not one of them. His two older brothers, Frankie and Lawrence – both the spitting image of Jamal – were selling crack from the age of fourteen and by sixteen were enforcing the debts with the aid of squeezy water bottles topped with hydrochloric acid. Two years of youth detention presented the opportunity to forge new acquaintances and revamp their business model, and when they were next arrested, three months after their release on licence, they were in possession of the proceeds of their expansion: two bored-out Russian Baikal pistols and twelve 9mm rounds. The mandatory minimum five-year custodial term was enhanced by the sentencing judge to eight, and the family's dissatisfaction with this result was what led to Jamal's mother declining to contact the family's usual firm when Jamal was arrested, and how Caz, covering the duty slot at the police station that night, had happily stepped in.

Jamal's learning difficulties were immediately apparent. Building a rapport and taking instructions has been a slow, delicate and, at times, near-impossible procedure, like extracting a tooth from a sleeping tiger without waking it. The omnipresence of Mama Lowton, at the police station, at Caz's offices and at court, has been both welcome and complicating. She has been a vital resource in filling in the narrative blanks in Jamal's backstory, yet Caz and I have been acutely mindful of the power that she wields over her boy's decisions. Any dissatisfaction on her part – however trivial and however ill-grounded – could manifest itself in even greater reticence in Jamal's dealings with us; worse, an application to transfer to a new firm.

After two sets of double doors, Caz and I break company at the stairs. She heads down towards the exit, I launch myself up two flights, two steps at a time, towards the robing room. I punch the door code and enter. Suitcases are sprawled on tables that stretch out as far as the eye can see. I locate mine and unzip the front pocket, fumbling through assorted biros for the orange Sainsbury's carrier bag wrapped around my cigarettes and my lighter. I remove two from the box and place them on the table, before re-wrapping and restoring the bag to its hiding place. This is my effort at self-restraint; if I keep cigarettes in my handbag, I know that they will be smoked on autopilot on my walk to and from the station. Zipping them away affords the best chance at successful rationing.

I quickly whisk off my gown, then my wig, and ball the two roughly next to my suitcase, before, slightly more tamely, unfastening my collarette and folding it neatly on top. Some colleagues gather outside to smoke still fully robed. I've never been convinced it's a particularly desirable look if a juror should fly the coop and catch sight of you puffing away in your regalia.

As I make for the door, I hear a familiar baying from behind the partition situated on the far left of the room, to mark out the silks' area. The voice is unmistakeably Baxter Wyatt. I don't linger to pick up the full contents, but his jeering appears to be directed towards Aliyah's opening. His audience – presumably Bob Evans – is evidently not responding in kind, as Baxter ups the ante from 'pedestrian' to 'snooze-fest' in an attempt to elicit a laugh. When this fails, he mounts a fresh horse. 'And what about that fucking intermediary, eh? What a waste of public funds . . .'

36

I head downstairs, through the atrium and out the revolving door into what has, since this morning's promise of sunshine, spoiled into a muggy autumn drizzle. Caz is standing alone under the canopy a few metres away, lost in thought, staring blankly towards a pigeon attending to the important business of attacking another pigeon.

She immediately boots into life as I approach and extend my hand towards her. She grabs one of the cigs and I light for us both. No words are exchanged. We both know the value of silence, enhanced by scarcity in the course of a trial like this. Multi-handed murders are chaotic at the best of times. A three-way cut-throat defence involving shifty opponents and a youth client whose functioning appears to have inured him to the reality of the evidence, and you have a headache that starts pulsing the minute you arrive at court and stalks you all the way home.

Because one thing is abundantly clear to both me and Caz: whether it is fear, or functioning, or teenage defiance, or whether it is simply that he knows he is guilty and lacks the wit to invent a tale to extricate himself, extracting meaningful instructions from Jamal has been a long slog, and there are still parts of the prosecution evidence that he is unable, or unwilling, to talk about. Parts to which we still have no answer. And we are going to need one. Because the snippet that the jurors have already heard is damning enough. Just wait until they hear the full details of the forensics. And the phones. Oh God, the phones.

Caz is evidently reading my mind. With smoke curling out of her nostrils, she offers her lawyerly assessment.

'He's fucked, isn't he?'

My silence betrays my agreement as I flick my butt on the floor and gesture towards the door.

CHAPTER 5

The Prosecution Opening

As the jurors return, doing their level best to remember the configuration in which they were sitting only thirty minutes earlier, the prosecutor rises, ready to continue.

The detail of the evidence to come must now be explained, colouring the spaces between the lines already drawn. And where Aliyah Arshad chooses to begin is with the CCTV, or, as she corrects herself following a pointed throat-clear from the bench, Closed Circuit Television camera footage, taken from various locations around Ableford town centre. When taken together with GPRS data extracted from the defendants' mobile phones, it is possible, she tells the jury, to track the defendants' movements on the night, up to and beyond their chance encounter with Bernard Hooper.

The jury will in due course be shown all of the relevant footage, curated by digital experts into an interactive compilation, Arshad promises, but for the purpose of this opening, it will suffice for her to summarise.

'Shortly before 11 p.m.,' she says, emphasising the *eleven*, 'Jamal Lowton arrived outside the "Reggie's" off-licence on Horcross Road. The footage shows him on his phone, and, indeed, moments later, a WhatsApp message was sent to Mr Lowton's good friend Arron Freeman, which said: "MT O REGG" – or, deciphering the text-speak, "meet outside Reggie's". Within a few minutes, Jamal Lowton was duly joined by Arron Freeman and Craig Mervyn-Scott.

'All three then entered the store, where the interior security cameras captured Arron Freeman, the tallest of the three, engaging in conversation with the cashier and purchasing alcohol, namely two bottles of Jägermeister.' She lands a hard J, which stirs an eyebrow from juror five – late teens or early twenties, but with a hairline adding a decade, pubescent blond moustache and black *Thunder-Cats* T-shirt.

'The quality of the recording is not the highest, but it is sufficient to clearly show the faces of all three defendants inside the shop – indeed, it is good enough for you to see Jamal Lowton casually smoking a rolled "spliff" of cannabis.

'The exterior camera at Reggie's records the defendants exiting the store and making their way slowly down Horcross Road and towards the town centre. Two features of this footage are significant. First, although you will hear toxicology evidence suggesting that the defendants had all consumed substantial quantities of alcohol and drugs, you can see from their gait and demeanour as they walk through the town that they are still very much in control of their senses. They are not falling over or staggering in disorientation. They are walking with purpose.' Hitting the plosives hard, Aliyah Arshad allows a moment's silence in which the question may be begged, before obliging herself.

'That purpose? I turn to the second relevant feature of this piece of footage: You can see, as the defendants walk away from Reggie's off-licence, that Craig Mervyn-Scott is carrying a navy-blue rucksack. That, the prosecution say, is what was used to transport the zombie knife, the weapon that they intended to deploy when the opportunity arose. And,' Aliyah teases, 'what else you will see from the footage is how intent the defendants were on finding such an opportunity. How hard they searched for their prey.' She looks up and logs juror seven's quizzical pout as confirmation that curiosity has been satisfactorily whetted, before gliding on.

The footage is not, the prosecution accept, continuous: not every building in Ableford is kitted out with security cameras. Instead, the jury will be invited to treat it as establishing key landmarks, around which other evidence can be fitted. The initial encounter between the defendants and Bernard Hooper, for instance, is not captured on camera, but what is available is a recording from CCTV on Rowe Street at 23:44, showing the three defendants walking in company with Bernard Hooper. Surrounding their prey, as the prosecution puts it. Craig Mervyn-Scott appears to be engaging Mr Hooper in conversation, although Arron Freeman and Jamal Lowton are showing an interest in whatever is being said.

Jurors summonsed to attend Ableford Crown Court can now hail from up to a forty-mile radius, the legacy of a court closure programme that auctioned the two sister Crown Courts in the county to the private developer with the deepest ministerial ties. Intimate knowledge of the charms of Ableford is therefore not guaranteed, and Aliyah Arshad takes a little time to deal with the geography, referring the jurors to an A3 map folded inside the large blue lever-arch files on their bench. Rowe Street, as the map shows, is a long road linking the concentrated town centre with Ableford's sprawling residential environs, not quite arterial but channelling a steady stream of traffic in daytime, which condenses to a trickle of returning commuters and a twice-hourly night bus after dusk. The lower reaches of its terraces variously cloister takeaways, off-licences, vape shops and second-hand electronics stores, some of which shoulder attached residential flats on their second and third floors. Again, the available CCTV does not afford universal coverage of the activity on the street outside, but those gaps can be filled in this case, the prosecution say, by two crucial eyewitnesses: Paul Bell and Farid Suhail.

'Paul Bell was at that time living in a second-storey flat directly opposite the junction of Rowe Street and Garth Yard. Farid Suhail was on the first floor of a property on Rowe Street, two doors down from Garth Yard. Garth Yard is a small, narrow side street – an alleyway, as both witnesses refer to it – that runs off Rowe Street. There are no cameras down this street – there is a derelict commercial premises and a run of large bins, and the alley is fenced off at the end. This,' Aliyah Arshad stresses, 'is significant. Garth Yard was chosen by the defendants as the place to which to lure Bernard Hooper precisely because they knew that what they planned to do would not be caught on CCTV. And because they knew that, once trapped in Garth Yard, there was nowhere for Mr Hooper to run.'

Aliyah Arshad proceeds to summarise what Paul Bell and Farid Suhail will tell this jury: the sights and sounds that violently rang in their respective New Years as they minded their own respective businesses. The people they saw and the acts to which they bore witness. The prosecutor seems to lean more heavily on Mr Bell's account for the detail; perhaps, the jury might surmise, because there was more that he could see from his vantage point. But she is in her element now, wrapping the strands of the anticipated witness testimony around the pillars of the prosecution's scientific evidence, as the eyes of the jurors widen and their pallor grows in tandem with the delicate, deliberate dripping of detail.

All of this evidence, she tells them, proves beyond doubt that the three defendants were each present and involved when the fatal blows were inflicted; when Bernard Hooper was killed 'for the grotesque entertainment of these three boys'.

41

CHAPTER 6

Arron (The Second Defendant)

My hands are still stiff from the cuffs. The screws took them off when they brought us back into court, but I keep finding myself shaking them, trying to get the blood pumping again. I look across at Craig, to see if he's doing the same. He's just sitting there with a face like he's got a proper mard on.

When we came back in and one of the screws told us to sit, Craig just stared at him, like 'Why, what's the point?' Like we didn't all know that any minute the judge was coming back into the room and that little guy with the glasses was going to shout 'ALL STAND!' And yeah, he's right. But there's no point in arguing. That's just Craig, though. You try telling Craig what to do – worse, you try telling him to wind his neck in, and it just makes him go zero to a hundred.

I'm not arsed, me. Sit, stand, whatever. Who gives a fuck?

One thing I don't get, though. I know we're Cat A. And obviously I know what they think we've all done. But the *cuffs*, every time we go out this dock and down the stairs to our pads, and every time we come back up again. What do they think we're going to do? Like, where are we gonna run? We've had near enough six months to sort shit, and we've waited until we're in court to just . . . what? For Craig to give Jamal a slap in front of all the barristers and tell him to stop being such a soft cunt? For me to give Craig a shove on them steps when we're going down?

Nah. I've got no problem with them two. As far as I'm concerned, we're sound. And I reckon they feel the same. I know they're both pointing the finger. But that's just the way it goes. I'm doing it to them. Nobody wants to grass up, but what's done is done. It's too late for any of us to change our stories. They're saying what they've got to say. I'm saying what I've got to say. That's just the situation. It's a minor. There's no point in causing grief.

That's the thing. I'm not actually a violent person. I know what it looks like, I do. But the person the prosecution is describing – that's not me. When she's telling the jury all them terrible things, saying those words – *savage, brutal, senseless slaughter* – I can't even get my head around it. It's like she's telling a story that just didn't happen. Like when you get proper wasted, and the morning after everyone is saying what you did, and you can't remember a thing but you're like *No way did I do that!* – and you don't know who's telling the truth and who's chatting shit. And then throughout the rest of the day, bits of your memory come back but other bits don't, and you're still trying to get the picture straight in your head.

Only this time I *know* what everyone is saying isn't true.

I look out the glass box at everybody in the court. There's two rows of them jurors, sitting to my right, and I'm looking at them but trying not to look at them. On the one hand, I want them to look me in the eye. I want them to see that I am not that person. But I don't want them to see me looking.

The prosecutor is still talking. She's going into all the details of why she says we've done what she says we've done. All this evidence that we attacked the guy for basically no reason.

She's telling the jury about CCTV from the offy, the new Reggie's

43

where I got the Jäeger and you can see all three of us together, and she says that you can tell from the way we walk out that we was all 'walking with purpose'. The big screen is showing photos of all us faces caught on camera. Jamal, man. Thick as fuck. I told him to put out his spliff. I didn't know at the time that he was just standing there, blazing in front of the camera like he's not even arsed, with his hands down his pants. It's probably because, whatever the prosecutor thinks, truth is that Jamal was mashed out his head. He didn't have a clue what was going on.

I realise that I'm shaking my head, and maybe even smiling a bit at the thought of that soft cunt, and I stop myself. I straighten my face and try to look serious again, but when I look up at the jury there's this posh-looking woman who's staring right at me.

Fuck.

The one thing my solicitor said to me over and over again was how important it is that I don't piss off the jury. 'Make a good impression,' he said.

Something about the way he said it, and the way he fiddled with his tie when he did – like he didn't realise he was doing it – reminded me of Graham. At the home, when they was preparing us for job interviews and that. And Graham would grab the knot on my tie and squeeze it and push it up til it was tight up against my neck – he wasn't rough with it, but it was firm – and he'd say, in his daft posh voice, 'You only get one chance to make a first impression.'

Well, my first impression with that posh lady is not going to be a good one. To be fair, it wasn't a good one I made for that first job interview either. I remember there was two people interviewing, upstairs in the drive-through on the Ricky Estate, a man and a woman, both wearing grey shirts and baseball caps, and the man had one of them badges with all the stars on it. And there was about

44

ten of us, sitting on chairs in a circle, and the woman said that what they were gonna do was ask a question and we'd then all have to answer it. Their first question was, 'Why do you think you'll be a good fit for McDonalds?' or something, and as the woman was speaking I realised that my chair was closest to hers, and I could see what was about to happen but couldn't do nothing to stop it. And sure enough, she pointed at me and said, 'Would you like to start us off?' and I just stared at them for what felt like an hour. My mouth was completely dry and in the end I just said the only thing that came into my head, even though it wasn't an answer to their question. It wasn't an answer to anything, but it just wouldn't get out of my head, and I thought that if I said it out loud, maybe my brain would free up space to think up a proper answer. So I just said, 'Your gherkins are proper rank', and they didn't say anything back. And I started laughing, cos I had no idea why I'd said it. And to them, I probably looked off my head. And that thought made me laugh even more. When I stopped laughing I said to the guy, I said: 'Mate, I know I haven't got the job, no worries', and I got up and shook his hand and went downstairs and got me a Double Quarter Cheese, and that was it. My first impression.

To be fair, it took a few goes before it got much better. I didn't do the best impression in my second interview. Or my third. Or for a fair few after that. But I got there eventually. And Graham was proper smug when I did. Like I was his own personal project, and my wins were his wins too. 'I told you,' he said. 'We'll make a man of you yet, Arron. You keep making the right decisions, and you're going be the best thing to come out of Wythenshawe since Marcus Rashford.' That were one of his favourite sayings, that.

And as I picture Graham's grinning face, all proud of what I done, I keep looking at the public gallery. Like he's sitting there, in his suit and his proper tied tie, watching over me. But he's not. Obviously. Even if he were still here, a court is the last place he's gonna find himself.

It's mad though that they're obsessing about Craig's backpack. The way the prosecutor is talking, it's like she's solved the case, like it's a brilliant point for the prosecution. And it's really not. But she doesn't know shit. Like, she says 'Jamal Lowton's *good friend* Arron Freeman', which is a joke. I know Jamal to talk to, but we're not friends. He's Craig's mate, not mine. We'll all chill together, but I don't feel anything for the kid. I don't know anything about him, other than he's a proper psycho when he's on the haze. Big joke in all this is that he didn't even need to be there that night. Life is about decisions, like Graham said. Jamal made a fucking bad one.

She's getting towards the worst bit now. I'm trying not to look at the jury's faces, but it's hard not to. It's all about meeting him and going to Garth Yard, and why we were there, and it's bullshit, of course, but at the same time it all – it all sort of makes sense when she says it like she does.

And on she goes. On about the knife, on about the injuries. On about how there were witnesses who could see bits of what was happening. Not all of it, but enough to show that we was all there, and that we're all guilty. And them words she's using again – *savage* and *brutal* and *senseless*. I can't help myself now, I have to look at the jury. And of course they're all looking at us, sitting in the dock. Their faces show what they're thinking.

And yeah, of course I was there. But that doesn't mean the prosecution witnesses are telling the truth. It doesn't mean that Craig and Jamal are telling the truth.

And it doesn't mean that the old fucker didn't deserve to die.